The New You!

Making the Grade

The Most Embarrassing School Moments EVER!

For best friends everywhere.

—J.H.

For Marianne, you always make the grade!

—T.M.

ISBN-13: 978-0-439-02014-5
ISBN-10: 0-439-02014-X

Text copyright © 2007 Scholastic Inc.
Illustrations copyright © 2007 Scholastic Inc.
All rights reserved. Published by Scholastic Inc.

12 11 10 9 8 7 6 5 4 3 2 1   7 8 9 10 11 12/0

Printed in the U.S.A.   40
First printing, October 2007

Friends 4 Ever

The New You!

Making the Grade

The Most Embarrassing School Moments EVER!

by Jo Hurley
Illustrated by Taia Morley

Scholastic Inc.
New York   Toronto   London   Auckland   Sydney
Mexico City   New Delhi   Hong Kong   Buenos Aires

Rachel

Name: Rachel

Nickname: Rach

Pet: Cat   **Hair:** Wavy

Favorite Thing to Read: Comic books

Favorite Person at School: Drama teacher

Favorite Article of Clothing: Peasant skirt

Best Dream: Win Academy Award

Worst Nightmare: Stage fright

Sam

Name: Samantha

Nickname: Sam

Pet: Dog   **Hair:** Bangs

Favorite Thing to Read: Sports stats

Favorite Person at School: Coach

Favorite Article of Clothing: Jean jacket

Best Dream: Olympic champion

Worst Nightmare: Broken leg

JESSIE

Name: Jessica

Nickname: Jessie

Pet: Turtle   **Hair:** Ponytail

Favorite Thing to Read: Anything!

Favorite Person at School: Librarian

Favorie Article of Clothing: Sweater set

Best Dream: Write a novel

Worst Nightmare: Computer crash

Name: Elizabeth

Nickname: Libby

Pet: Guinea pig   **Hair:** Curls

Favorite Thing to Read: Teen magazines

Favorite Person at School: All my BFFs

Favorite Article of Clothing:
Can't pick just one!

Best Dream: Helping a charitable cause

Worst Nightmare:
Bad hair day

Libby

Why Me?
Welcome to the Hall of Shame

Everyone gets embarrassed at some point. Whether it's taking a spill or spilling the beans, embarrassment is inevitable. Although the humiliating state of embarrassment is just about too much to bear anywhere, it's especially hard when something happens at school. There's nothing worse than finding yourself red-faced in a school assembly, in the middle of a soccer game, or up close with the cutie-pie classmate whose locker is located next to yours.

A few realities about getting embarrassed at school:

1 There will always be someone there to laugh at you.
Crowds in the auditorium, spectators in the gymnasium, kids in the school yard, and even the dreaded hall monitor! Wherever you turn at school, someone may be watching—and taking notes. Of course, in those crowds are your best friends, a principal who cares, and scores of other supporters. So there's a good chance your embarrassing moment may not make the front page of the school paper. Then again . . .

ha!

ha!

ha!

Teachers have radar.

Ever try to fib your way out of a missed homework assignment (i.e., "the dog ate it!")? Teachers seem to be born with built-in truth detectors. If something embarrassing happens—they're sure to notice. You can only hope they won't announce it over the loudspeaker.

3 This place is all about grades.

You are not just in any ordinary location. You are in a place where everything you do is rated on a scale from A to F. Do they give report cards for embarrassing moments? How about extra credit? What would your grade be?

Blush-O-Rama

Imagine this: You're standing in line at the cafeteria when a group of kids decides to start a food fight. Who's the unlucky girl caught in the middle? You! How can you possibly keep cool when you have strawberry yogurt—and who knows what else—dripping down your shirt? What's a girl to do?

Everyone reacts differently to embarrassment. Some kids toss their heads and laugh it off. Others run for the nearest janitorial closet.

What do you do?

One time in gym class, my stomach started rumbling and everyone in class started to laugh. I was totally, utterly, one-hundred-and-one-percent mortified. My gym teacher said I could be excused. But when I went into the hallway to recover, the principal saw me! She marched over to me with this angry look. "Take off that makeup!" she said. I had to explain to her that it was just me, not makeup. That's what happens to me when I get embarrassed and upset: I turn red all over.

As a performer, I try not to let anything embarrass me. But there are those moments, those horrifying moments, when embarrassment finds me. That's when I turn into an ice cube. I was onstage once and my costume ripped. Then I forgot my lines. It was one bad thing after another and I just froze. Lucky for me, it was the end of the show and no one really noticed.

I ADMIT IT. I GET EMBARRASSED EASILY. TOO EASILY. AND IT SHOWS. BOY, DOES IT SHOW. IF I'M GIVING A PRESENTATION IN CLASS AND SOMEONE COUGHS OR LAUGHS OR MAKES THE LEAST LITTLE SOUND, I LOSE MY CONCENTRATION. THEN I GET NERVOUS. AND THEN I START TO STUTTER. ONCE I EVEN GOT THE HICCUPS.

When I'm super embarrassed, my friends usually try to reach out and make me feel better. But don't even think about holding my hand! The littlest embarrassing episode gives me the sweatiest palms in school. I can't even hold a pen—it just slips through my fingers, literally. Uh...does anyone have a towel?

Sure Signs a Person Is Embarrassed

(Check off all that apply to you.)

Once you're embarrassed... There's no escape!

- [ ] Sweaty palms
- [x] Red cheeks
- [ ] Twitching
- [ ] Sweaty lip
- [ ] Pale as a ghost
- [ ] Stuttering
- [ ] Bug-eyed
- [x] Can't speak
- [ ] Repeats, "Oh, wow, I am soooo embarrassed!" over and over and over and over and... you get the idea.

Teacher's Pet—NOT!

This year at school I'm getting A-s and high praise from my teachers. But don't be fooled; I'm no teacher's pet. No way! Some of my most mortifying moments at school have been in front of my teachers. There is nothing worse. Do any of these embarrassing events sound familiar?

Check the bottom of each page and rate the embarrassing moments.

But It's Snot Funny!

My math teacher is always cracking jokes. One day, he gave us this pop quiz and he kept laughing about it. He didn't understand why we were all shaking in our sneakers. But the quiz was tough! I remember sitting there with my face in my hands, wondering why I hadn't studied harder. Then he cracked one of his jokes and I started to laugh—hard. My eyes were watering, I was laughing that hard. Then, all of a sudden, the teacher pushed a tissue in front of me. I looked up and said, "What's this for?" Before he could answer, a kid in the row next to me said, "For the giant booger hanging out of your nose." The teacher just nodded. I grabbed the tissue and tried not to look humiliated.

Rate this tale on the Embarrass-O-Meter.

A: Actually...not too bad

B: Blush-worthy, but survivable

C: Call the Embarrassment Police.

D: Don't look now but all eyes are on YOU.

E: Find the nearest hole and crawl into it, okay?

Spaghetti Surprise

I was standing in the lunch line at school, waiting for them to refill the vat of spaghetti. My music teacher came up and started talking to me. While we were chatting, the lunch lady handed me my plate of food. But then disaster struck. The kid behind me wasn't paying attention. He walked into me. I lost my grip on the plate. The spaghetti slid off, landing right on my teacher's shoes with a very loud splat.

Rate this tale on the Embarrass-O-Meter.

A: Actually...not too bad

B: Blush-worthy, but survivable

C: Call the Embarrassment Police.

D: Don't look now but all eyes are on YOU.

E: Find the nearest hole and crawl into it, okay?

Mum's the Word

WE WERE ALL IN ENGLISH CLASS TALKING ABOUT THE READING LIST. EVERYONE WAS TALKING AT ONCE. I KEPT SAYING, "EXCUSE ME!" TO GET MY TEACHER'S ATTENTION, BUT IT SEEMED LIKE SHE DIDN'T HEAR ME OR SHE WOULDN'T LISTEN TO ME. AFTER ABOUT FIVE MINUTES I GOT REALLY FRUSTRATED. "MOM, WOULD YOU LISTEN TO ME!" I SHOUTED. A SPLIT SECOND LATER, I REALIZED WHAT I HAD SAID. ONLY A FEW KIDS HEARD ME, BUT THEY TEASED ME ABOUT IT FOR A WEEK. ONE KID STILL SAYS TO ME BEFORE CLASS EVERY DAY, "ARE YOU GOING TO CALL FOR YOUR MOM TODAY?" GRRRRRR.

Rate this tale on the Embarrass-O-Meter.

A: Actually...not too bad

B: Blush-worthy, but survivable

C: Call the Embarrassment Police.

D: Don't look now but all eyes are on YOU.

E: Find the nearest hole and crawl into it, okay?

Daydream Believer

At the start of every school year, we play a game to make sure the teacher knows everyone's names. As we were playing the game in history class, I started spacing out. By the time the teacher called on me, I was daydreaming about this movie star I like. So when she said, "Name?" to me, I called out the actor's name. Everyone did a double take. I quickly blurted out my own, real name, but it was too late. Everyone was already laughing.

Rate this tale on the Embarrass-O-Meter.

A: Actually...not too bad

B: Blush-worthy, but survivable

C: Call the Embarrassment Police.

D: Don't look now but all eyes are on YOU.

E: Find the nearest hole and crawl into it, okay?

She'll Fall for Anything

One afternoon, I left math class with my hall pass and headed to the bathroom. It was the very end of the day and I didn't really feel like being in class, so I took my time walking there. On the way back, I started goofing around. What harm could it do? No one was there. I began spinning in the hall, around and around like a top. The only trouble was, I lost my balance—big time. I got so dizzy that I slammed right into a door. It popped open and I fell into the room. It just happened to be the teachers' lounge, and the principal was standing right there!

Rate this tale on the Embarrass-O-Meter.

A: Actually...not too bad
B: Blush-worthy, but survivable
C: Call the Embarrassment Police.
D: Don't look now but all eyes are on YOU.
E: Find the nearest hole and crawl into it, okay?

The Big E Word Search

We got together and made a list of all the things that come to mind when we think about getting embarrassed. Can you find them in the word search puzzle below? Search up, down, sideways, backwards, and diagonally. And when you find all the words, the only remaining letters will be Es (for embarrassment, of course!). Answers on page 63.

Blush   Disgrace   Mortify   Squirm
Crush   Humiliate   Run   Wail
Cry   Laugh   Shame
Disappear   Moan   Shrink

S	Q	U	I	R	M	E	D	E	E
C	E	B	E	K	W	A	I	L	E
M	R	L	E	N	E	E	S	C	E
O	H	U	M	I	L	I	A	T	E
R	E	S	S	R	E	R	P	E	S
T	E	H	E	H	G	E	P	E	H
I	E	C	E	S	E	R	E	E	A
F	R	E	I	H	G	U	A	L	M
Y	E	D	M	O	A	N	R	E	E

Gym Class Catastrophes

Save me!

On a scale of one to ten (with one being the least and ten being the most), I'd say that gym class has a potential embarrassment factor of . . . well . . . ELEVEN. Face it: Where else is it possible to lose your shorts, get elbowed in the head, or trip over your own sneaker laces? I've had my share of gym class catastrophes. Trust me. Don't pretend like you haven't had some, too. Rate the following scenarios for humiliating potential.

Ready, Aim, BONK

Everyone knows I'm not a sports star. Actually, I'm kind of a nerd when it comes to gym class. But I still try my best. There was one class, however, where no amount of trying could help me. I stood ready at second base when we played softball, but when someone hit a line drive, I ducked. I ducked!!! As if that wasn't bad enough, a few innings later, someone threw the ball to me from the outfield and it went through my legs.

Double—
how could this have happened?

Single—
don't worry, you're cool.

Triple—
almost the worst, but you're still hanging on!

Home Run—
the ultimate embarrassment!

A Lap in the Face

Being the best at sports is very important to me. So when I was picked as the leadoff at the intramural swim meet, I was excited. I stood on the starting block, adjusted my swim cap and suit, took a deep breath, and—dove. It was an awesome dive and I slid right into the water. My strokes were strong all the way down the lane. But what I didn't realize was that my dive had been a false start. Everyone else heard the coach's whistle and got back out of the pool. Not me. I swam an entire pool length by myself—when I should have turned back. When I finally came out of the water, everyone was applauding and not in a good way. It was hard to start over after that.

Double—
how could this have happened?

Triple—
almost the worst, but you're still hanging on!

Single—
don't worry, you're cool.

Home Run—
the ultimate embarrassment!

Lemme Into My Locker!

Last week I was late for gym class and I raced into the locker room without looking. First I practically slid on a wet towel right into a bench. Then I couldn't open my locker lock. I was banging hard on the locker to try to get it open when someone pointed out that I was banging on her locker and not mine. Whoops. As if that wasn't bad enough, when I finally did get into my own locker, class had already started. I pulled on my sneakers fast and tried to sneak in without being noticed, but my stupid sneakers squeaked all the way across the gym floor. Talk about an entrance.

Double—
how could this have happened?

Triple—
almost the worst, but you're still hanging on!

Single—
don't worry, you're cool.

Home Run—
the ultimate embarrassment!

squeak

Embarrassment Insta-Polls

What's worse: ripping the seam on your gym shorts in front of the class bully or in front of your secret crush?

Getting embarrassed in front of someone I like is worse than being dunked in boiling oil. Okay, maybe not that extreme . . . but it's pretty bad!

What's worse: falling as you kick the soccer ball or kicking and missing the ball completely?

WHY IS THERE NO GRACEFUL WAY TO FALL? ONCE YOU'RE IN MOTION, THERE'S NO WAY TO STOP THE CLUNK AS YOU HIT THE GROUND. I HATE THAT!

What's worse: being the slowest or the klutziest on your sports team?

Even though I'm good at sports, I've been slow and klutzy way too many times to remember. Ugh.

What's worse: gym clothes that are too big or too small?

Once my mom left my gym clothes in the dryer for too long and my T-shirt shrank—a lot. Thankfully, Jess loaned me her extra shirt in time for class.

Crushed!

Zowie!

Pow!

Ooof!

THwack!

BLam!

There are sooo many ways to get crushed at school. You can do poorly on a test—after you studied as hard as you could. You can get snubbed by a friend—after she decides to hang out with someone you don't like.

Here's a sampling of some seriously crushing moments we shared together. The only reason we can talk about it today (without turning watermelon red and wanting to poke our heads into the sand) is because we had one another. Friendship is the only ship that sails right through embarrassing moments. Let's face it: We'd be sunk without one another. Don't you and your BFFs agree?

I keep a notebook with my most secret thoughts. Usually I leave it at home . . . in a secret place that I don't reveal to anyone—not even my friends. For some reason, it ended up in my school backpack that day. I must have mixed it up with my school notebooks. When I opened my bag, the notebook flipped out onto the floor of my math class. That wouldn't have been a major problem if I'd seen it. But I didn't. Someone else did. The next thing I know, two boys behind me are laughing out loud, reading some of the pages. I grabbed it as fast as I could, but the damage was already done.

What Got Crushed:
My Privacy!

Our art teacher took a bunch of classes to a museum for an afternoon field trip. I was so excited. I love seeing paintings up close. It's much better than just looking at pictures in a textbook. But the best part of this trip was that I saw my crush there. During the museum tour, I stared at him the entire time. But in the middle of a lecture, the teacher caught me staring. He said, "Miss Jessie, how about keeping your eyes on the painting instead of your classmates?" He didn't name names, but everyone knew who he was talking about, including the guy in question. Gulp.

What Got Crushed:
MY HEART!

I'm not an official member of the school choir, but I do love to sing. The school had a talent show last year and I decided to perform a solo. My mom helped me pick out this pretty pink satin gown. I got onstage and sang every note perfectly. It was one of the highlights of my life, I swear. But as soon as I started to walk away, my shoe caught in the hem of the dress. I fell forward flat on my face. I got a fat lip in front of my entire school and I didn't win the talent show, either.

What Got Crushed:
My Ego!

I have never been excited like I was on the day the coach picked me to be a starter on the soccer team. I felt like I was walking on air. Everyone congratulated me in the halls. As I was leaving school, this crowd of other soccer players high-fived me in the school lobby. I slapped their hands and kept right on walking. The only trouble was . . . I walked right into a plate glass door that I thought was open. Obviously, it wasn't.

What Got Crushed: My Face!

Purple Spit, a Terrible Zit, and Assorted Fashion Disasters

School is tough enough. And we aren't perfect. But that doesn't mean we don't keep trying to be perfect. Everyone feels fashion challenged from time to time. But there are some of us who feel it all the time. Sometimes the most awkward school moments are the ones that start inside (and outside) our own bodies. And when it comes to burps, bumps, and bad clothes, we know what we're talking about.

Ewww! What did we do?!

Pen Pal? Nope! More Like the *Pen-emy!*

I thought it was the perfect day. I was sitting in class, dressed in my favorite hoodie, working on a book report. Usually when I write, I chew on the end of my pen. Today, I was doing that when I felt this splurt. Before I could do anything to stop it, the purple ink from my pen exploded all over my hoodie and my face. It looked like someone hit me in the face with a paintball. Not a pretty sight.

Are you kidding me?!!
Anything fashion-related is
MAJOR with a capital M.

Slammed

Everyone was in the hall talking between classes. I was gabbing with Jessie because our lockers are right next to each other. We were laughing about something and I wasn't really looking at my locker. When I slammed it shut I didn't notice that Jessie's hand was *right there*. Ouch. She screamed. Everyone stared. There should have been a neon sign turned on over my head that read, DORK. That's what I felt like. Luckily, Jessie's hand was okay.

minor major

Thankfully, major embarrassment was averted— but only because Jessie played it so cool. Sometimes friends can be helpful in these situations . . . very helpful.

The New Zit Revue

Last year during the holiday performance at school, I had a solo. It wasn't very long, but I wanted to make the most of it. That day I woke up to find a zit the size of a volcano on the tip of my nose. My mom loaned me some cover-up but no matter how much I put on, it only seemed to make the pimple more noticeable. By the time of the performance that night, I swear it had doubled in size. Everyone called me Rudolph.

minor major

This one would be absolutely major for me! What would <u>you</u> do?

had a very shiny nose . . .

Bed Head

I DON'T KNOW HOW THEY TALKED ME INTO IT, BUT RACHEL AND LIBBY CONVINCED ME TO WEAR MY HAIR DOWN FOR THIS BIRTHDAY PARTY ONE SATURDAY. I SPENT THE ENTIRE MORNING WASHING, CURLING, AND SETTING IT, SO IT WOULD LOOK JUST RIGHT. A-ND THEN I DID THE UNTHINKABLE. WHILE I WAS WAITING FOR THEM, I FELL ASLEEP IN MY DAD'S BIG CHAIR. WHEN THEY SHOWED UP, I RACED OUTSIDE TO MEET THEM. LIBBY'S MOUTH FELL OPEN. "WHAT IS *THAT?*" SHE ASKED ME AS I CLIMBED INTO HER FAMILY'S CAR. I REACHED BACK AND FELT A WAD. MY HAIR WAS SNARLED AND FELT GLUED TO THE BACK OF MY HEAD. LUCKILY, RACHEL HAD A BRUSH WITH HER, BUT NOTHING WE DID COULD CHANGE THE FACT THAT MY HAIRDO WAS A MASSIVE HAIR *DON'T*.

WHAT COULD HAVE BEEN GRAND-SCALE EMBARRASSMENT TURNED INTO MINOR STUFF THANKS TO BFF INTERVENTION. WHEW.

What's Your EQ?

Take this easy quiz to reveal your EQ (embarrassment quotient). After each question, read the sequence of answers. Choose which one is most like you. Answer key on page 40.

1 **You're in math class when your pencil drops on the floor. You reach down to get it, but your shirt is caught on the desk. The entire desk goes down to the floor with you!**

(a) You laugh out loud. After all, it must have looked pretty silly.

(b) You scream out loud, "I can't believe I just did that!"

(c) You say nothing. You don't even move. Embarrassment paralyzes you.

(d) You start to cry. How will you ever get unattached from this desk?

2 Oh, no! Your school bus changed routes and someone forgot to tell you. Coming home from school in the afternoon, you miss your stop completely.

(a) Go up to the bus driver and tell him what happened.

(b) Stand up in your seat and say, "Wait! I missed my stop! We have to stop! I missed my stop!"

(c) Stay in your seat until the last stop. Then you tell someone.

(d) Get off at the next stop and walk home in tears.

3 Your history teacher walks around the classroom, calling on students to raise their hands when they know the answers. As soon as you hear a question you know for sure, your hand shoots up into the air. The only problem is . . . your teacher is standing right there and you just punched him in the nose.

(a) You and your teacher laugh at the accident together.

(b) The teacher winces in pain and you stand up and gush, "I'm sorry, I'm sorry, I'm soooooo sorry!" twenty times in a row.

(c) You freeze in position, staring at his nose.

(d) First you gasp and then you sob. In moments, your teacher is sending you to the nurse for being so upset.

4 The school lunch was kind of gross today. In the middle of art class, your tummy starts rumbling, and not in a good way. As class goes on, the stomach noises get louder and louder and . . .

(a) You make a joke about it, pretending that you're about to explode, and then ask to be excused.

(b) You make a funny face and move your chair so it makes a bigger noise than your stomach.

(c) You silently rub your stomach, hoping the noise will go away.

(d) You get up quickly, trying not to cry, and make a beeline for the girls' bathroom.

5 At the lockers, you and your friends are gossiping about other girls. Loudly you talk about a girl in your gym class who looked like a "total dork" today. Then you notice the girl is standing right behind you.

(a) You slap the girl on the shoulder and say, "Oops! Just kidding!"

(b) You cover your mouth with mock horror and then say, "Where did YOU come from?"

(c) You turn back around and pretend you never saw her.

(d) You turn beet red, start coughing, and run away.

While standing up at the board during math class, you start moving from side to side. Your sneakers squeak loudly. Of course, everyone in class thinks the noise is something else.

(a) You point to one of your friends in the first row and chuckle. "Mary, was that you?"

(b) You quickly start dancing around even more so the sneakers squeak again—and again.

(c) You don't move. In fact, you're still standing there when the class bell rings ten minutes later.

(d) You turn toward the board and hold your breath so you don't throw up.

 It's your school's musical revue and you're part of a group dance number. Backstage is chaos while everyone gets ready. You're racing around in costume, waiting to go on, when a teacher grabs you. "Get out there!" the teacher says. Without thinking, you trot onstage but soon discover you've been pushed into someone else's dance group.

(a) Throw your hands into the air, twirl around, and smile anyway.

(b) Try to mix into the other dance group, copying their moves and hamming it up for the audience.

(c) Make like you're playing freeze tag and you just got tapped.

(d) Run directly across the stage and disappear.

8 During lunch, you're gazing out over your tray when you spot a cute classmate across the cafeteria waving at you. Of course, you wave back. But moments later, you realize the person was waving at someone else.

(a) You throw your hands into the air and pretend to stretch.

(b) You wonder aloud if you should leave school for the day. Excuse? Utter mortification.

(c) You cross your arms tightly to your chest.

(d) You make a mental note to never wave again. Ever.

9 One morning you glance at the school calendar and discover that it's Pajama Day! Quickly you change out of your jeans and put on a pair of flowered pajama pants, a cami T-shirt, and your big fuzzy slippers. However, when you arrive at school, no one else is wearing pajamas—and you forgot to bring a change of clothes.

(a) Make jokes all day about your outfit and how you think there should be two pajama days.

(b) Rehearse a long-winded, ten-minute excuse about mixing up the dates and having nothing to wear.

(c) Hide in the bathroom for most of the day.

(d) After the first pajama joke, dissolve into tears and have the school call your mom to come pick you up.

10 It's after school and soccer practice just ended. You head for the girls' bathroom. Inside the stall, you start singing to yourself. In the middle of your reverie, however, you hear someone laughing. Oh, no! You're not alone!

(a) You laugh, too. After all, if you can't laugh at yourself, who can you laugh at?

(b) "Who's out there?" you shout, hoping to scare the person away.

(c) Lift up your legs so no one can see under the stall and hope that the giggler doesn't hear—or giggle—anymore.

(d) Quickly get out of that bathroom and run all the way home.

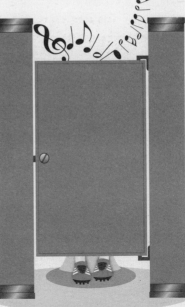

Turn the page to find out your true EQ!

What's Your EQ?

Answers:

If you answered mostly As, your EQ is low, way low. You don't really get embarrassed much. If you are embarrassed, you quickly defuse an explosive situation with laughter.

If you answered mostly Bs, your EQ is on the rise. You find ways to get over the embarrassment, but you still call attention to it. In some ways, being embarrassed isn't so terrible. It still puts you in the spotlight.

If you answered mostly Cs, your EQ fluctuates from low to average to over-the-top. Different situations embarrass you differently, but your reactions tend to be the same. Sometimes you just stand still, hoping to keep a low profile. Other times you stand still, hoping that embarrassing things will just go away.

If you answered mostly Ds, your EQ is off the charts. You're close to tears and on the run no matter what happens. Try to relax, will you? It can't be that bad!

Cafeteria Laffeteria!

Mystery meat, lumpy mashed potatoes, rubbery carrots, and Jell-O with drippy whipped cream. Mmmm. What could be worse than an unappetizing school lunch? An embarrassing moment in the school cafeteria, of course! Not only are there lots of opportunities in the lunchroom for freaky food experiences, it's one of the main places in school where everyone sits together. Anything can happen here. All you can do is try to laugh about it—that is, unless someone else laughs at you first.

May I Have a Sip?

My friends and I were eating lunch one day when Libby asked for a sip of my juice. Instead of offering it to her, I thought it would be funnier to chug it. That way, I wouldn't have to give her the sip. But when I started chugging, everyone at the table began making funny faces. Soon I was laughing so hard that I choked and the drink came exploding out of my nose, all over the table and my friends, especially Libby. Everyone stopped laughing and started giving me a really hard time.

Yours embarrassingly, S

(Maybe if I sign off with just my first initial, no one will know the story is from me.)

How Embarrassing Is This?

 No biggie.

 It only hurts for a minute.

 I need to lie down —now.

 Take me to the emergency room.

All Mixed Up

IN THE MIDDLE OF LUNCH I FELT SICK, SO I HEADED FOR THE BATHROOM. ON THE WAY THERE, I FELT BETTER, SO I TURNED AROUND AND WENT BACK TO OUR LUNCH TABLE. BUT THE GOOD FEELING DIDN'T LAST. A FEW MINUTES LATER, I GOT UP AGAIN. EVERYONE AT MY TABLE WAS MAKING JOKES BEHIND MY BACK. BUT THAT WAS ONLY PHASE ONE OF THIS EMBARRASSING MOMENT!

NOW, KNOWING I WAS ABOUT TO THROW UP, I RAN TO THE BATHROOM, NARROWLY MISSING A COLLISION WITH ONE OF THE LUNCH MONITORS. WHEN I FINALLY PUSHED THE BATHROOM DOOR OPEN, HALF-DAZED, I REALIZED MY WORST MISTAKE OF ALL: I WAS IN THE BOYS' ROOM!

YOURS WITH A RED FACE AND SWEATY PALMS,

Jessie

How Embarrassing Is This?

No biggie.   It only hurts for a minute.   I need to lie down —now.   Take me to the emergency room.

Splat!

Last week the lunch special was turkey and mashed potatoes. Everyone else said it looked gross, but I didn't mind, so I waited for my serving. But then, in the middle of the line, someone ahead of me started flicking his potatoes into the air. He was trying to hit his friend, but before I knew it, I was wearing a shirt full of gravy. Naturally, the lunchroom monitor was nowhere to be found.

Rachel

How Embarrassing Is This?

No biggie.

It only hurts for a minute.

I need to lie down —now.

Take me to the emergency room.

Whoops!
I Did It Again!

Why is it that in the movies, when some clumsy high school kid drops a tray of food in the cafeteria, forks clang and everyone claps a little, but that's it? The reality of the whole tray-dropping scenario is sooo much worse. When I dropped a tray in the cafeteria, the entire lunchroom jeered and cheered my name—loudly. I think I turned five shades of red and then—lucky me—someone from the school paper took a photograph. I was so mortified by what had happened that I made a beeline for the lunchroom door. But on my way down the hallway, I realized that I was still carrying the red cafeteria tray. What did I do? Go back and return it. Everyone was still cheering when I got there. . . .

Yours with sheer horror,

.... **How Embarrassing Is This?** ....

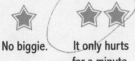

No biggie.   It only hurts   I need to lie down   Take me to the
              for a minute.   —now.   emergency room.

I Can't Believe You Called Me That!

Embarrassment comes in all shapes and sizes. Sometimes we get embarrassed because of things we do. Other times it's because of things we say. And then there are those embarrassing moments when we want to shrink up into a ball, squeeze our eyes shut, and forget we exist because of something other kids say. File these embarrassments under: Oh, Will You Just Shut Up?

Worst of the Worst

Embarrassing Nicknames You Must Promise Never to Call Someone Else

WORM HEAD. Some kid called me this all summer at soccer camp. He was just jealous because I could do a great diving kick. When it comes to names, I'm opposed to any slimy references. Remember that.

I'M LUCKY. I DON'T REALLY HAVE ANY NICKNAMES EXCEPT FOR JESS. BUT WHEN I WAS IN FIRST GRADE, THE CLASS BULLY CALLED ME PIGGY. I CRIED FOR A WEEK. IT STILL BRINGS BACK BAD MEMORIES.

A kid in drama club once called me WART for obvious reasons that are too horrible to recount. However, that experience proved that pointing out blemishes on a person should be considered cruel and unusual punishment. Don't you agree? I mean, would you want to be called ZIT or HIVE? Please.

The most embarrassing name anyone ever called me was LIBBY the LOSER. I was not then, nor have I ever been, a loser, so that nickname was waaaaay off. But it was still a teeny bit embarrassing. No one wants to be called a loser.

How to Cope When the Cruel Clique Calls You Something Embarrassing

Plot revenge? Well, Jessie has a few smart ideas, but we know revenge is wrong.

Sass 'em back? Sam says, "Yeah!" but we know that it's not a good idea to start a war of the evil nicknames.

Curl up in a ball and cry? Well, maybe just for a minute. But do it privately. And work on a quick recovery.

Tattle? No way. Telling on someone just makes a bigger deal out of it, and you want this incident to go . . . poof!

Ignore it? *Ding!* That is the right answer. Whenever someone tries to make you feel embarrassed or sad by calling you a name, just ignore them. No one has the right to make you feel bad. You're great! If you ignore them, they'll be the ones feeling embarrassed for having said something so dumb.

Don't Try This at Home!

So far we've established that there are plenty of ways to get embarrassed at school. And just when you think it's safe to go back again . . . something even MORE dreadful happens. Now it's time for you to rate each embarrassment on your own blush-o-meter.

If you were in our shoes . . . what would you do? Use the blank lines to write down your most creative anti-embarrassment tactics and excuses.

_____

_____

_____

_____

_____

A Fool for Drool

Last night you hardly slept, and today you faced a devastating pop quiz, an inedible lunch, and a study hall monitor who almost sent you to the principal's office for snoring. Now you're riding back home on the school bus and before you know it, you're asleep. But you're not alone. You've fallen asleep on the shoulder of some older kid who isn't even in your class! And what's worse . . . you're drooling!

Now what? Do you . . . politely wipe off the drool?
Stay asleep and pretend nothing happened?
Freak out? What?

Go Before You Zip

It's the big day of the school play, *Alice in Wonderland*. You have the exciting role of caterpillar. The costume, weighing as much as you, is very awkward to wear. And once the zippers are zipped, you're stuck inside for the entire play. There's just one eensy-weensy problem: You forgot to go to the bathroom. And the longer you stand onstage, the harder it gets to keep your cool. When it's time for you to speak your lines, you draw a total blank.

Now what? Do you . . .shuffle offstage in the middle of the scene? Sweat it out? Make up something to say? What?

First Prize Goes to ... Klutzy

It's the afternoon of the big science fair and you've won a prize.
Your mom is there. Your grandfather is there. Teachers and students
are staring at you as you go get your trophy. But then what seems
like an ideal moment of glory turns into a disaster. As you reach
the stage, your shoe catches on the table, sending you into
the principal, who is handing out trophies. The entire table of
trophies smashes to the ground. One flies off the stage and
hits another teacher in the head. The entire room bursts into
laughter. And just when you think it can't get any worse,
you notice that the whole thing is being videotaped.

Now what? Do you . . . crawl underneath the trophy table?
Scream at the top of your lungs? Start laughing and wave at
the camera? What?

Stuck on You

You started the morning badly. You marched into the wrong classroom and got lost again on the way to the right classroom. Now you're feeling a little jumpy. Is everyone staring at you? In the middle of class you sit on your hands and at some point (you're not sure when), your hands end up behind you, in between the metal bars of the chair you're sitting on. That's when trouble really begins. You try to pull them out to write something down, but they're stuck. And no matter how hard you wiggle, you're stuck. Moments later, the teacher is standing over you, trying to help, but it's no use. She tries a little soap and water so you can wriggle free, but that doesn't work, either. The next thing you know, the teacher says, "Well, I guess we have to call in the fire department."

Now what? Do you . . . try to bite your hand off like a wolf stuck in a trap? Tell the teacher you want a second opinion? Ask everyone in the class to pull as hard as they can? What?

Ayyyeeeiiiiiiooouuu!*

And Other Cries for Help

Our parents and pals always tell us to stand tall and not worry about "what other people think." Ha! We know the truth: When embarrassing moments happen at school, sometimes it's impossible to think fast or act smart. Here are some of our best ideas on how to cope. . . .

*Translation: High-pitched, desperate squeal of embarrassment

When embarrassed, ask friends to make a DISTRACTION so the attention is focused away from you. That's where my drama skills come into play.

SWITCH GEARS! Start jumping around or talking gibberish so people will forget the other really embarrassing thing you just did. Of course, there is always the risk this action will be more embarrassing than the first. But I'm a risk-taker, aren't you?

PRETEND that the embarrassing incident never happened. Flip your hair and change the subject.

DON'T RUN. DON'T HIDE. JUST BRUSH IT OFF AND ACT COOL. THE ULTIMATE STATEMENT TO MAKE AFTER DOING SOMETHING EMBARRASSING: "I MEANT TO DO THAT." BECAUSE, OF COURSE, YOU DID.

RELAX ... Or Else

There are a few ways to deal with the stress that comes with embarrassing moments. You can do some simple things to relax your body and mind right there in school, between classes.

Breathe Deep. Stand or sit still, close your eyes, and take in a deep breath through your nostrils. Let it out slowly from your chest. Do this at least five or six times. Feel any better?

Watch Your Posture. Your grandmother probably always told you to "sit up straight!" She was right. When you have kinks or cramps in your shoulders or back, it's hard to relax or stay focused. Sitting up properly also helps you to breathe easier.

Brush Your Teeth. Between the easy motion of brushing teeth and the cool sensation of mint toothpaste and water on the gums, your body will feel more relaxed.

Take Notes. Grab a blank journal or notepad and write down everything that's stressing you out. Don't censor yourself. Express your feelings about a situation rather than pushing them down inside.

De-Stress Success

Can you curb embarrassment before it even happens? Take good care of your body, mind, and heart. When some embarrassing incident arises, you need to feel so secure that nothing will get you down. Trust us, we've been there.

Before Exams

• It may sound obvious, but STUDY. The more prepared you are, the better your chances of facing a test with no stress.

• Get SLEEP. A few ZZZs make all the difference in the way you think and act.

• Break it down into PIECES. Think small so you do work in manageable amounts. Otherwise, you could send your brain into overdrive.

With Friends

• Be ASSERTIVE. Let people know how you feel and what you think, but in positive, reaffirming ways. If you start yelling, everyone gets stressed out, including you.

• Accept ENCOURAGEMENT. Let your network of best buds compliment you. When someone says, "Good job!" just say, "Thank you."

• Get MOVING. Dance, exercise, or even shop till you drop. Plan activities that keep you moving and keep your friendships—and your self-esteem—strong.

• TALK about it. Confide in friends about your aspirations and fears. Sometimes just admitting how you get embarrassed is enough.

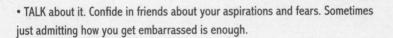

On the Go

• PRACTICE before heading into a stressful situation. For example, if you have to speak in front of your class, rehearse it in front of your parents or friends first.

• Just take a BREAK. Have a cold drink, get some fresh air, or close your eyes for a minute to refocus and stop stressing!

• Learn to SAY NO. Don't be afraid to tell people you can't do something without becoming overwhelmed. Of course, you can't say "no" to homework assignments, as tempting as it may be.

Top 10 Quicky Comebacks

Or, How to Recover Gracefully from Your Most Embarrassing Falls, Flubs, and Flip-Outs

1 "Who put that _____ there?!" Fill in the blank with words like "big, clunky shoe" or "banana peel." Good for using at home when deflecting blame onto younger brothers or sisters.

 2 "D'oh! I've got two left feet!" Pretend to be goofy and klutzy, even when you aren't. You could even do a little jig. Just don't fall down twice.

3 "Don't look at me!" Immediately telling bystanders to look at something other than you sometimes works well.

4 "Does anyone have a bag I can put over my head?" Use humor at all times. It is the ultimate embarrassment cure.

5 "If you think this was embarrassing, you should have seen what I did yesterday!" Take a moment to create the illusion that whatever embarrassing thing you just did pales in comparison to the much more embarrassing thing you did at another point in time.

"Don't worry. I'm okay." Make a big deal and pretend like you almost got really hurt. This way everyone around you will worry and lend support rather than analyzing how dumb you looked falling flat on your face.

 "Who asked you?" Before someone has a chance to insult you, cut them off.

 "Thanks for not laughing." Before someone has a chance to crack up hysterically, convince them not to laugh. Sincerity works best.

"Gee, I guess my superpowers aren't working today." That should be good for another laugh.

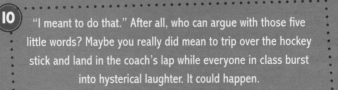 "I meant to do that." After all, who can argue with those five little words? Maybe you really did mean to trip over the hockey stick and land in the coach's lap while everyone in class burst into hysterical laughter. It could happen.

EEP!

The Embarrassment Emergency Pack

Just in case!

Manage your next embarrassing episode with the grace of a ballerina, the endurance of a soccer star, and the smarts of a class president. Here are some of the key items you may want to keep stashed away in your school locker, just in case!

Chewing gum. Keep away embarrassing death breath.

Fresh Breath Chewing Gum

Extra T-shirt. This is a key garment to have on hand should you be the target of a) a lunchroom food fight, b) an exploding pen, or c) throw-up (don't ask).

spring-fresh Deodorant

Foot sanitizers and deodorant. No one likes smelly feet or armpits, except maybe your dog.

Large poncho or cape. Good for quick getaways from embarrassing moments or whenever paparazzi are chasing you. As if that ever happens.

Zit cream. Nuff said.

Zit-Zap Cream

Bandages. Keep paper cuts and skinned knees covered.

Mini-packs of tissues.
There is nothing worse than a sneeze without a target.

Tissues

Help! Stop! You're Embarrassing Me!

Use these pages to write down the best and worst embarrassing moments of your school career. And spare no embarrassing details, please!

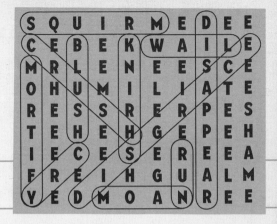

A Special Note to Our New Friend (aka YOU):

Of course we don't wish embarrassing moments on anyone, but if they do come . . . at least you can be prepared! Remember: No one is perfect. As our grandmothers used to say, "Don't worry. Everything comes out in the wash."

Chances are that people who witness any embarrassing event starring you will forget it five minutes later. Just when you think things look grim, the sun comes out and turns the gray around. Trust us. We're speaking from lots of experience. Have fun! Hang tough!

LIFE GOES ON . . .

No matter how embarrassing things may get . . .

And on and on . . .

Just like Friends 4-Ever!